A NEW
HEALTHY YOU!

Dairy Free

igloobooks

igloobooks

Published in 2017
by Igloo Books Ltd
Cottage Farm
Sywell
NN6 0BJ
www.igloobooks.com

All imagery: © iStock / Getty images

HUN001 1017
2 4 6 8 10 9 7 5 3 1
ISBN 978-1-78810-617-7

Cover designed by Nicholas Gage
Edited by Jasmin Peppiatt

Printed and manufactured in China

Contents

Introduction

What are the benefits of a dairy-free diet? Is it worth the effort? Does your health suffer if you drink milk? Why are so many people nowadays choosing to leave the lactose out of their latte?

For many years, people have actively reduced their consumption of meat products and have sometimes opted to cut out animal products entirely. This is often a decision based on ethics, but more and more it is becoming a matter of health. Milk and other dairy products have well-documented effects on the human body, and a dairy-free diet is often extolled for its benefits to the skin, nasal and aural passages, as well as digestive and immune systems.

Missing out on milk?

Where once a dairy-free diet might have simply meant missing out on milk-based products, that is no longer the case. The advent of milk substitutes and calcium-enriched drinks – and even supplements for people who are lactose-intolerant – means that you can devise a healthy food plan from all the necessary food groups that is both tasty and full of variety. These products are becoming much more widely stocked, so you no longer have to visit specialist health food stores – or avoid high-street coffee shops. Soya hot chocolate, anyone?

What's milk made of?

The main ingredient in milk is water, but it also provides carbohydrate, protein, fat and minerals. There is evidence that a typical supermarket pint can contain less desirable substances, which may be cause for concern.

Natural ingredients

The sweetness in milk comes from lactose, a simple sugar or carbohydrate. Milk also provides protein in the form of casein and whey proteins, as well as vitamins and minerals, including the well-known 'bone maker' calcium. It also has phosphorus, magnesium, potassium, sodium, iodine, selenium, zinc, iron and copper.

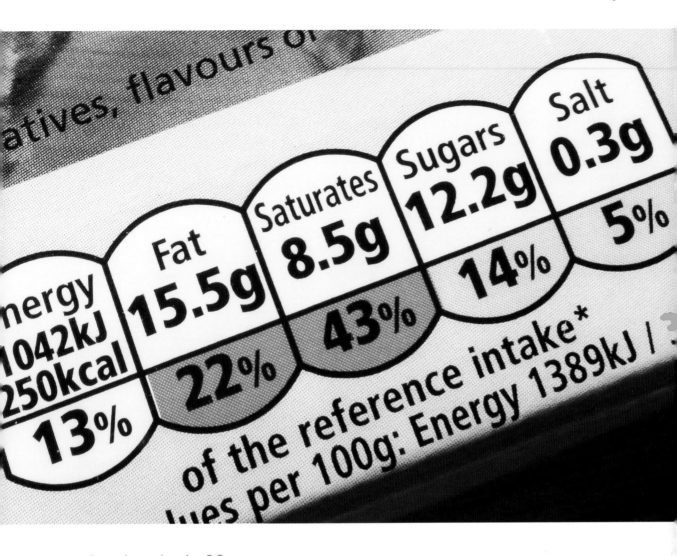

tives, flavours o...

Energy
1042kJ
250kcal
13%

Fat
15.5g
22%

Saturates
8.5g
43%

Sugars
12.2g
14%

Salt
0.3g
5%

of the reference intake*
...lues per 100g: Energy 1389kJ |

The bad stuff

A high proportion of the fats in milk are saturated, which may cause raised cholesterol levels and an increased risk of heart disease. Butter has little or no lactose but is mainly fat, with little nutritional value. However, it's not only the fats that are a worry. Cows' milk naturally contains a variety of hormones and chemicals that stimulate growth in young calves. Whether or not these ingredients are actually bad for humans is the subject of much debate, and opinions are divided right now.

The good news for dairy-lovers is that organic milk shows fewer traces of these additives, and fans of raw (non-pasteurised) milk claim that it contains higher levels of the beneficial nutrients and bacteria that our bodies need.

Say goodbye

Some people decide to bid farewell to dairy products to improve their overall well-being. Dairy products – especially cheese, butter and cream – can contribute hugely to our intake of unhealthy saturated fats. By eliminating these animal by-products, people can significantly reduce their fat intake, which will lower their cholesterol levels and may prevent weight gain. Cutting down on dairy may also help to get rid of many unwanted symptoms of ill health, both external and internal, as explained in the following pages.

Eating ethically

Some people may choose to maintain their normal eating habits, but gradually incorporate small changes in their diet. One way of doing this is to eliminate one type of dairy each week, so the task of going 'dairy-free' isn't so overwhelming.

Others may choose a more drastic change to their diets: vegetarianism and veganism are growing in popularity, due to their health benefits and concerns with the environment and animal welfare. The concept of veganism was developed from the desire to cut out all animal products from the diet. Rearing animals for food uses vast amounts of resources such as water, fodder crops and pasture land for grazing. Using the land for crops for human consumption instead of animal feed is much more productive and less damaging to the ecosystem.

However, the dairy-free diet can be enjoyed with or without meat products – the choice is yours!

Allergy or intolerance?

Many people have allergies – more than a quarter of the population are affected to varying degrees. Dairy or milk allergies, however, are thankfully rare. It is much more likely that physical reactions to food are caused by an intolerance to one or more basic ingredient.

A milk allergy is caused by the body's immune system reacting to an element in the milk, usually one of the proteins (casein or whey). It releases antibodies to fight this element, which is seen as unwanted. The symptoms can be the same as they are in many other food allergies, including swelling of the mouth or face, wheezing, a rash and, in very extreme cases, anaphylaxis. They may also mirror the digestive complaints listed on the following pages. Allergy sufferers need to be vigilant about avoiding all dairy products, even in tiny amounts.

Different tolerances

Milk intolerances don't involve the immune system. Instead, the body cannot process elements in the milk – sometimes the proteins, but more commonly the lactose.

Suffering varies in its intensity from person to person. Some feel discomfort while others may be doubled up with cramps. People also have different thresholds of tolerance. While one person might struggle even to have milk in their tea, others can cope with small amounts now and then.

Are you intolerant?

The symptoms of dairy intolerance are similar to those of many complaints, so you need to establish what is at the root of the problem. If you suspect that milk is to blame, cut out dairy produce for three weeks and then gradually reintroduce items one at a time, starting with the most innocuous, for example bio yogurt or hard cheese. Keep a note of your body's response as you slowly begin to try dairy products again. Then see your doctor or a registered dietitian to share the results and get further advice.

ACNE

Research suggests that consuming milk and whey products can aggravate acne. Milk products can raise insulin levels and levels of IGF-1, a naturally occurring growth hormone, which can then lead to over-production of sebum, the oily substance that clogs pores.

External signs

Dairy produce has been connected to skin and respiratory complaints, including psoriasis, eczema, hives, asthma and sinusitis. Similarly, it is thought that an excess of dairy in the diet exacerbates glue ear and hay fever. Dairy is said to cause an over-production of mucus, which blocks the passages, and inflammation, which makes the problem worse. The jury is out on how much effect dairy has on this set of problems, but it seems certain that a healthy, vitamin-rich, low-fat diet can improve all of these ailments.

Digestive disorders

The most common symptoms of a digestive problem include some – but probably not all – of the following: bloating, excess gas (flatulence), diarrhoea, constipation (children are often affected this way), stomach cramps, nausea, swollen ankles and puffy or dark-circled eyes. These problems may be caused by indigestible lactose remaining in the gut. It begins to ferment, which leads to varying degrees of stomach discomfort, water retention and swelling.

Development disabilities

Some experts are convinced of a link between dairy intolerance and conditions such as autism and Asperger's syndrome. In less obvious cases, many children who suffer from lack of energy, aching limbs, distended stomach and mouth ulcers have been found to benefit greatly from the removal of dairy from their diet.

Health facts
– is it safe?

Humans are the only creatures on Earth that drink the milk of other species. This realisation may be enough in itself to send you in a dairy-free direction. Globally, around 70% of the adult population is thought to have a dairy intolerance, and the proportion is much higher in some parts of the world.

REALLY RARE

True allergic reactions to milk are rare, affecting only one or two per cent of people. Although severe and frightening, they can also change and lessen, with some affected children growing out of their allergy altogether.

First food

All mammals are designed to suckle in order to get the nutrition they need to grow. Babies produce an enzyme called lactase, which allows them to break down milk sugars (lactose). However, this enzyme is produced in smaller and smaller quantities as the child (or calf or cub or kitten) grows. The result is that adult mammals cannot easily digest these sugars. Believe it or not, most adult cats are lactose-intolerant, despite the stereotype of a cat lapping up a saucer of milk.

This lactose intolerance is exactly the situation for a proportion of weaned humans. Lactase persistence (the continued ability to produce lactase) is genetically determined and is most common in the traditional dairy farming regions of the world — notably, Europe and North America. Lactose intolerance rates are extremely high in cultures that do not rely on dairy produce. Up to 95% of Asian, African and Hispanic people have little or no ability to digest lactose after they are weaned off their mother's milk.

Easy does it

So, armed with the facts, you may have decided already to do without dairy and feel the benefits. If so, there are some key factors to consider. Some people start slowly, leaving the cheese off their pizza or having spreadless sandwiches. Make a list of all the dairy items you eat regularly and cross off the product you could easily live without. Losing an item or two each week will not seem like a hardship at all.

Read the label

If you are intent on eliminating dairy entirely, you will need to become label-savvy. Check the ingredients list on every item before you buy it – you will be surprised how many foods have 'hidden' milk products in them. However, you will also learn early on that the same product, made by different manufacturers, may or may not contain dairy items. The recipes of some products change and develop, so what could be a no-no one year might find its way back onto your 'yes' list after a time.

Shop around

All products are not created equal! It's purely
a matter of personal taste. If soya milk doesn't
tempt your taste buds, try rice milk or coconut
milk. If you don't like one variety, try another.
One brand of almond milk can taste subtly
different from the next, as it may contain other
ingredients, such as vanilla extract, sugar or
natural sweeteners, which will affect the taste.

Dangerous drinking

Take care when you look for an alternative to
milk as a simple thirst-quencher. It's easy to
fall into the trap of replacing milk with drinks
that can cause damage in other ways. Most
fruit-based drinks are loaded with sugar
and 'empty' calories, which supply a quick
burst of energy but have no nutritional value.
Fizzy drinks, especially caffeinated ones such
as cola, are even worse. They may actually leach
minerals from our bones, lowering bone density
and increasing the risk of fractures
and osteoporosis.

ADDED BONUSES

Reducing the amount of dairy in your diet has also been shown to help relieve the
symptoms of endometriosis (a condition of the female reproductive system) by lessening
the inflammation of the affected areas caused by dairy foods. Cutting down on dairy
also benefits smokers who are trying to quit, as it helps to stop the build-up of mucus
at the start of the process.

Milk mates

Many of the recipes in this book leave out any semblance of dairy produce, including milk substitutes. There will be times, though, when you really need a splash of the white stuff – whether it's in your tea, to make a sauce or to pour on your cereal in the morning. So what are the options?

If you are lactose-intolerant, you can simply use lactose-free milk or take lactase tablets before consuming regular dairy produce. The former has added lactase, and both options break down the lactose that your body finds hard to handle. Consult your doctor first, before taking lactase tablets.

Milk substitutes

The most common substitutes for milk are plant-based.
Milk can be extracted from many things: soya beans,
rice, oats, coconut, quinoa, nuts (almonds, hazelnuts,
cobnuts, cashews, brazil nuts) and even potatoes and
hemp. Coconut milk has a delicious, distinctive taste
and is excellent for cooking.

Soya milk is the most widely available and versatile
alternative to cows' milk and it offers about the same amount
of protein. However, it has lower levels of digestible calcium
than cows' milk, so it is often calcium-enriched when sold in
cartons. Soya milk is also made into other products, such as
cheese, cream and yogurt.

Hemp milk is thick and can be grainy. It provides less
calcium than cows' milk but has high levels of omega-3
fatty acids, which are good for the heart.

Rice milk is as white as its dairy relative but quite thin,
so better for drinking or pouring than for cooking. It is
fairly low in protein, as are many nut milks.

Oat milk is low in fat and usually enriched with vitamins
and calcium. It has a slightly sweet taste and makes a great
drink, as well as offering a good alternative to cows' milk
in cooking.

EVERYTHING IN MODERATION
Be careful when introducing dairy alternatives,
especially as a remedy for certain physical symptoms.
Too much of the alternative can overload the system in
a new way, leading to similar, negative reactions.

Don't lose out

It is important that cutting out dairy from your diet – whether for intolerance issues or general health and lifestyle reasons – does not mean you miss out on vital nutrients. You must be sure that your new regimen replaces the dairy food group with a variety of other nutrient-dense foods.

Milk, thanks to the calcium it contains, has long been linked to having healthy teeth and bones. It is true that children need to build strong bones to serve them in their adult life (when bone production turns to bone deterioration). Calcium is also essential for other areas of body maintenance – namely, blood clotting and nerve and muscle function. Dairy products, however, are by no means the only source of calcium.

Using soya milk and bio yogurt

Soya milk contains far fewer calories than regular whole milk but around six times less calcium. However, these days it is generally sold fortified with extra calcium. Be sure to shake the carton before you pour – studies have shown that the calcium settles at the bottom, and an unshaken portion of soya milk provides much less calcium than is indicated on the nutrition breakdown. You should also look out for calcium-enriched orange juice.

Try introducing plain bio yogurt, or good-quality live yogurt, into your diet. Their long fermentation time means that most of the lactose has already been broken down by the bacteria in the yogurt, saving your body the work. Natural yogurt is rich in calcium and available in low-fat varieties. Be wary, though, of long-life or UHT yogurt – it is no longer 'live', so contains no bacteria. Kefir is a fermented milk product, often in the form of a drink, which may also be easily tolerated because of its lactose-consuming bacteria.

Look, too, for recipes that contain calcium-rich ingredients, such as leafy greens, beans and pulses, and snack on nuts to increase your calcium intake. A handful of sesame seeds or a drizzling of molasses on salads, cereals and desserts will provide an additional boost.

The bones of it

Calcium is vital for healthy teeth and bones – but it cannot work in isolation. Your body also needs both vitamin D, to help absorb the calcium, and a good amount of weight-bearing exercise.

The bright stuff

Vitamin D is essential for bone health and can also protect against colds and depression. Comparatively few foods contain vitamin D, so you have to find other ways to get it. The very best way is from sunshine – just 20 minutes in the fresh air on a sunny day will do the trick (and make you feel great too). Don't let your skin burn and be aware that darker skin needs longer exposure to produce a decent amount of the vitamin. Unfortunately, it has to be direct sunlight – it won't work if you are indoors, even behind a window.

You can buy vitamin D supplements, although there is still some debate about how effective these are. Vitamin D can also be found in oily fish, egg yolks, liver and fortified foods such as breakfast cereal, soya milk and orange juice.

Be active

Bones are made up of living tissue and need to be exercised to keep them strong. Regular exercise in youth will help to increase bone mass, and the right sort of activity will prevent bone loss as you age. Swimming and cycling don't contribute, as they are not 'weight-bearing' exercise. You need to be working against gravity to reap the rewards: tennis, walking, jogging, golf and dancing are all good choices. Resistance exercise such as weight training also helps, and gardening, housework and even lifting the shopping count as well.

BRITTLE BONES

Osteoporosis is a condition that weakens bones, making them more likely to fracture. It affects many people, especially in old age. Bone density is determined in your youth and you reach your maximum bone mass around age 30. After this, bone mass gradually starts to decline.

Milk by any other name

As you embark upon your dairy-free journey, you will need to learn how to spot milk and its relatives, in all of their forms. It may seem obvious to avoid cream, cheese and butter, but watch out, too, for dairy in disguise!

People with a true milk allergy will need to be sure they are not exposed to the wrong products in any form. If you are intolerant, you may be able to get away with small amounts of exposure without drastic consequences. Once tested and diagnosed, you will know whether your body reacts to lactose or to milk proteins. Soon, you will become an expert in reading food labels, but remember that ingredients may change – so, check the packaging every time you buy.

Look for these key dairy giveaway terms in the ingredients listing:

- whey/whey protein/whey sugar
- hydrolysed whey
- casein/caseinates
- hydrolysed casein
- buttermilk
- ghee
- curds
- crème fraiche
- quark
- rennet
- lactalbumin
- lactose
- milk solids
- lactic acid (E270)
- lactobacillus
- lactoglobulin

Pre-packaged problems

Many off-the-shelf products contain milk derivatives when you least expect them. Breadcrumbs, batter and butter-basted products are common culprits. Be especially careful when you buy any of the following:

- sausages, ham, turkey/chicken slices, coated fish/chicken products, pizza, pies, paté
- crisps, dips
- sweets, cakes, biscuits, crackers, ice cream, gelato
- bread, crumpets, muffins, breakfast cereals, pancakes
- stock, gravy, table sauces, salad dressing, cooking sauces
- instant potato
- some beer and wine
- pills and medicines

To really be sure of what you're eating, cook from scratch!

THE GOOD NEWS
Dark chocolate is likely to be lactose-free and even entirely dairy-free. Hurrah! The higher the cocoa content, the less likely it is to cause problems – aim for 70% or above. Always be sure to check the label first.

Milk myths

Mention the 'm' word and you will doubtless find that many people are self-proclaimed nutritionists, with dairy produce a specialist subject. Don't believe all you hear, however...

Whole milk is the worst for lactose intolerance

False. The proportion of lactose in skimmed and semi-skimmed milk is around the same as in whole milk, making the 'lighter' versions no better than full-fat milk.

A dairy-free diet can include eggs and cheese

True and false, depending on your reasons for being dairy-free. Eggs are not classed as dairy – they contain no lactose – so can be eaten if you have an intolerance or allergy, but not if you have chosen a vegan lifestyle. Similarly, hard cheeses such as Edam, Cheddar, Parmesan and Emmental have very little lactose left in them, so may suit those with intolerances.

Goat's milk isn't as bad as cows' milk

Again, it depends. Goat's milk – as well as buffalo's milk and sheep's milk – are from animal sources, and contain both lactose and milk proteins. However, it is thought that these non-cows' milks are digested more completely and so are more easily handled by the body. You may be able to drink goats' milk, depending on your particular allergy or intolerance.

Dairy-free products are no good for cooking with

False – but you have to become substitute-savvy. Some dairy-free spreads and fats can be used in baking, but you will find that your cakes' ability to rise will vary between products. Rice milk can be slightly gritty, coconut milk has a distinctive taste that may not suit some recipes, soya milk is creamy but cannot be whipped, and thinner milks don't always produce great sauces. Likewise, some dairy-free cheeses melt well and are great for pizzas and pasta dishes. Several hard dairy-free cheeses make poor sandwich fillers, but work well in cooking.

Healthy checklist

It is patently clear that you should not simply remove dairy items from your diet without finding nutrient-rich foods to take their place. Don't despair, though, if you are forced to find alternatives because of an allergy or intolerance – there are so many delicious ingredients just waiting to be discovered!

You have read about the importance of calcium. Fortunately, it is easy to find the mineral in many different foods other than dairy. Choose protein-packed beans – white, kidney and black-eyed – and look for lentils, chickpeas and other pulses and legumes, which will boost both your omega-3s and fibre. Nuts (especially almonds), dates, figs, prunes and dried apricots are great for calcium, too.

Healthy alternatives

One of the best food groups for calcium is leafy greens. Kale, okra, broccoli, watercress, spring greens and pak choi are all excellent vegetables to choose from, although be sure not to overcook them and wipe out any nutritional value.

Look to the sea for more calcium-rich content. If you are not taking the animal-free route, cook with sardines and pilchards, anchovies and tinned salmon – in other words, fish that still contains some bones. You could also try some seaweed! It's full of calcium, fibre and iodine.

Apart from calcium, it is important to ensure that you get enough protein from non-milk foods. Meat and eggs are prime sources, but if you are also cutting them out, try to include vegetarian proteins such as tofu, tempeh and edamame beans. Grains such as quinoa and amaranth are great sources and versatile. Nuts and nut butter (look for low-sugar varieties without hydrogenated oils), and many seeds (sesame, sunflower, poppy, chia and hemp), all up your protein intake.

EATING OUT

Finding the right restaurant can be tricky, but keep cultural differences in mind for a dairy-free experience. The lack of milk in Japanese and South-east Asian cuisines makes their restaurants a good bet for your dairy-free requirements.

Breakfasts and brunches

Get that 'get up and go' feeling with the delicious, dairy-free breakfasts and mid-morning dishes in this chapter.

Breakfast is so important – it will prepare you for the day ahead and give you the early morning nutrition boost that your body needs. Make sure your breakfast is varied otherwise your diet will suffer if you stick to the same set of breakfasts and brunches.

Planning and preparation are vital so remember to add to shopping lists before you go to the supermarket and try to think ahead. You don't want to get out of bed in the morning and not have the key ingredients for your dairy-free breakfast.

There are a whole range of inspiring dishes in this chapter, from the refreshing Berry Smoothie Bowl and Banana and Walnut Muffins to Coconut and Honey Pancakes, which are very filling and delicious! This chapter even includes a dairy-free Full English Breakfast, which is sure to keep you feeling full for hours!

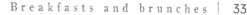

SERVES : 2

Preparation time: **25 minutes**

Berry smoothie bowl

50 g / 1 ¾ oz / ¼ cup chia seeds

28 g buckwheat porridge flakes

500 ml / 17 ½ fl. oz / 2 cups almond milk

150 g / 5 ½ oz / 1 cup frozen summer berries

2 tbsp maple syrup

TO GARNISH

1 handful fresh berries

2 tbsp goji berries

2 tbsp chia seeds

2 tbsp pumpkin seeds

2 tbsp sunflower seeds

1. Stir the chia seeds and buckwheat flakes into the almond milk and leave to thicken for 20 minutes.

2. Transfer to a liquidizer and add the berries and maple syrup and blend until very smooth.

3. Pour into two bowls and arrange the berries and seeds on top.

SERVES : 1

Preparation time: **5 minutes**

Freezing time: **1 hour**

Spinach and banana smoothie

2 bananas, chopped

2 kiwi fruit, peeled and chopped

35 g / 1 ¼ oz / 1 cup baby leaf spinach

250 ml / 9 fl. oz / 1 cup apple juice

1. Spread the banana and kiwi fruit out on a greaseproof paper lined baking tray and freeze for at least 2 hours. It can then be transferred to a freezer bag and stored for future use or used straight away.

2. Put the spinach in a liquidizer with the apple juice. Blend until smooth.

3. Add the frozen banana and kiwi and blend again until smooth, then pour into a glass and serve immediately.

SERVES: 1-2

Preparation time: **5 minutes**

Cooking time: **25 minutes**

Full English breakfast

2 tbsp sunflower oil

2 good quality pork sausages

1 large tomato, halved

2 rashers bacon

1 tbsp dairy-free butter

4 button mushrooms, halved

125 g / 4 ½ oz / ½ cup baked beans

2 large eggs

toast, to serve

1. Heat 1 tablespoon of oil in a frying pan. Fry the sausages over a low heat for 15 minutes. Transfer the sausages to a plate and keep warm in a low oven.

2. Season the cut side of the tomato. Fry the tomato cut side down in the frying pan next to the bacon rashers for 5 minutes, turning the bacon halfway through.

3. Meanwhile, melt the dairy-free butter in a small saucepan and fry the mushrooms with a pinch of salt and pepper for 5 minutes.

4. Transfer the mushrooms, bacon and tomatoes to the sausage plate and keep warm in the oven.

5. Gently heat the baked beans in the mushroom saucepan while you cook the eggs. Add the other 1 tablespoon of oil to the frying pan and fry the eggs for 3 minutes.

6. Return all of the ingredients to the frying pan and reheat for 2 minutes or until everything is piping hot.

7. Serve immediately with toast on the side.

MAKES : 400ML

Preparation time: **10 minutes**

Blueberry soother

3 medium beetroot, cut into chunks

2 oranges, peeled

100 g / 3 ½ oz / ²/₃ cup blueberries, plus extra to garnish

1 large ripe banana, peeled

mint leaves to garnish

1. Process the beetroot and orange through an electronic juicer, according to the manufacturer's instructions.
2. Transfer the juice to a liquidizer and add the blackberries and banana.
3. Blend until smooth, adding a handful of ice cubes to chill if preferred. Pour into glasses and serve immediately, garnished with blueberries and mint leaves.

SERVES: 4

Preparation time: **15 minutes**

Cooking time: **30 minutes**

Coconut and honey pancakes

250 g / 9 oz / 1 ²/₃ cups plain
   (all purpose) flour

1 tbsp ground flax seeds

2 tsp baking powder

2 large eggs

300 ml / 10 ½ fl. oz / 1 ¼ cups coconut milk

2 tbsp coconut oil

100 ml / 3 ½ fl. oz / ½ cup manuka honey

150 g / 5 ½ oz / 1 cup raspberries
   and blackberries

1. Mix the flour, ground flax and baking
   powder in a bowl and make a well in the
   centre. Break in the eggs and pour in the
   coconut milk then use a whisk to gradually
   incorporate all of the flour from around
   the outside.

2. Melt the coconut oil in a frying pan then
   whisk it into the batter.

3. Put the oiled frying pan back over a low
   heat. You will need a tablespoon of batter for
   each pancake and you should be able to cook
   3 pancakes at a time in the frying pan.

4. Spoon the batter into the pan and cook for
   2 minutes or until small bubbles start to
   appear on the surface. Turn the pancakes
   over with a spatula and cook the other side
   until golden brown and cooked through.

5. Repeat until all the batter has been used,
   keeping the finished batches warm in a
   low oven.

6. Pile the pancakes onto warm plates, drizzle
   with honey and scatter with berries.

SERVES: 4

Preparation time: **5 minutes**

Cooking time: **8 minutes**

Apple, cranberry and cinnamon porridge

600 ml / 1 pint / 2 ½ cups soya milk

125 g / 4 ½ oz / 1 ¼ cups rolled porridge oats

2 tbsp manuka honey

2 eating apples, cored and chopped

50 g / 1 ¾ oz / ¼ cup dried cranberries

2 tsp ground cinnamon

1. Mix the soya milk with the oats in a saucepan, then stir over a medium heat until it starts to simmer.

2. Add the honey and a pinch of salt then reduce the heat to its lowest setting and continue to stir for 5 minutes.

3. Divide the porridge between four bowls and top with apple, cranberries and cinnamon.

SERVES: 6

Preparation time: **10 minutes**

Cooking time: **1 hour**

Honey granola with fresh berries

75 ml / 2 ½ fl. oz / ⅓ cup manuka honey

75 ml / 2 ½ fl. oz / ⅓ cup apple juice

1 tbsp sunflower oil

175 g / 6 oz / 1 ¾ cups rolled porridge oats

75 g / 2 ½ oz / ⅔ cup pumpkin seeds

50 g / 1 ¾ oz / ½ cup sunflower seeds

2 tbsp flax seeds

100 g / 3 ½ oz / ½ cup raisins

600 ml / 1 pint / 2 ½ cups dairy-free yogurt

300 g / 10 ½ oz / 2 cups strawberries,
    blueberries and raspberries

1. Preheat the oven to 160°C (140°C fan) / 325F / gas 3.

2. Stir the honey, apple juice and oil together in a bowl with a pinch of salt then toss it with the oats and seeds.

3. Spread the mixture out on a large baking tray and bake for 1 hour, stirring every 10 minutes to ensure it all toasts evenly. Leave the granola to cool completely, then stir in the raisins.

4. Serve the granola topped with dairy-free yogurt and plenty of fresh berries.

SERVES: 2

Preparation time: **25 minutes**

Coconut cacao smoothie

50 g / 1 ¾ oz / ¼ cup chia seeds

25 g / 1 oz / ¼ cup desiccated coconut

500 ml / 17 ½ fl. oz / 2 cups coconut water

2 bananas, sliced and frozen for
  at least 2 hours

2 tbsp pure cacao powder

2 tbsp dried coconut flakes

2 tbsp cocoa nibs

1. Stir the chia seeds and desiccated coconut into the coconut water and leave to thicken for 20 minutes.

2. Transfer to a liquidizer with the bananas and cacao powder and blend until very smooth.

3. Pour into two glasses or jars and top each one with a spoonful of coconut flakes and a spoonful of cocoa nibs.

SERVES: 2

Preparation time: **10 minutes**

Cooking time: **20 minutes**

Dairy-free rice pudding

1 tbsp dairy-free spread

85 g / 3 oz / ½ cup pudding rice

250 ml / 8 ½ fl. oz almond milk

1 tsp vanilla paste

2 tbsp pure maple syrup

2 tsp cinnamon

2 tsp nutmeg

1. Melt the dairy-free spread in a large heavy bottomed saucepan before adding the rice, milk, vanilla and half the syrup. Stir the mixture together and reduce to a very low heat. Cook gently for 30 minutes or until the rice is tender and the mixture has thickened and become creamy.

2. Spoon into serving bowls before topping with the remaining syrup, cinnamon and nutmeg.

SERVES : 1

Preparation time: **2 minutes**

Cooking time: **2 hours**

Green super smoothie

2 bananas, chopped

2 kiwi fruit, peeled and chopped

35 g / 1 ¼ oz / 1 cup baby leaf spinach

250 ml / 9 fl. oz / 1 cup apple juice

1. Spread the banana and kiwi fruit out on a greaseproof paper lined baking tray and freeze for at least 2 hours. It can then be transferred to a freezer bag and stored for future use or used straight away.

2. Put the spinach in a liquidizer with the apple juice. Blend until smooth.

3. Add the frozen banana and kiwi and blend again until smooth, then pour into a glass and serve immediately.

Preparation time: **25 minutes**

Cooking time: **18 minutes**

Banana and walnut muffins

3 very ripe bananas

110 g / 4 oz / ⅔ cup soft light brown sugar

2 large eggs

120 ml / 4 fl. oz / ½ cup sunflower oil

225 g / 8 oz / 1 ½ cups plain
 (all-purpose) flour

2 tsp baking powder

100 g / 3 ½ oz / ¾ cup walnuts, chopped

2 tbsp runny honey

1. Preheat the oven to 200°C (180°C fan) / 400F / gas 6 and line a 12-hole cupcake tin with paper cases.

2. Mash the bananas with a fork then whisk in the sugar, eggs and oil. Sieve the flour and baking powder into the bowl and add two thirds of the walnuts.

3. Stir just enough to evenly mix all the ingredients together then divide the mixture between the paper cases and scatter the rest of the walnuts on top.

4. Bake the muffins for 18 minutes. Test with a wooden toothpick, if it comes out clean, the cakes are done. Transfer the cakes to a wire rack and drizzle with honey. Leave to cool completely before serving.

MAKES: 12

Preparation time: **25 minutes**

Cooking time: **18 minutes**

Blueberry muffins

1 large egg

125 ml / 4 ½ fl. oz / ½ cup sunflower oil

125 ml / 4 ½ fl. oz / ½ cup soya milk

375 g / 12 ½ oz / 2 ½ cups self-raising flour, sifted

1 tsp baking powder

200 g / 7 oz / ¾ cup caster (superfine) sugar

150 g / 5 oz / 1 cup blueberries

1. Preheat the oven to 180°C (160°C fan) / 350F / gas 4 and line a 12-hole muffin tin with paper cases.

2. Beat the egg in a jug with the oil and soya milk until well mixed.

3. Mix the flour, baking powder, sugar and blueberries in a bowl, then pour in the egg mixture and stir just enough to combine.

4. Divide the mixture between the cases, then bake in the oven for 18 minutes. Test with a wooden toothpick, if it comes out clean, the cakes are done. If not, test again in 5 minutes.

5. Transfer the cakes to a wire rack and leave to cool completely before serving.

MAKES: 400ML

Preparation time: **10 minutes**

Freezing time: **3 hours**

Strawberry linseed shake

2 ripe bananas, peeled and sliced

150 g / 5 ½ oz / 1 cup strawberries, hulled

2 papaya, cut into chunks and
    seeds removed

3 pink grapefruit, peeled

1 tbsp golden linseeds, plus an extra sprinkle
    to garnish

mint to garnish

1. Spread the banana and strawberries out on
   a baking tray and freeze for 3 hours or
   until solid.

2. Process the papaya and grapefruit through
   an electronic juicer, according to the
   manufacturer's instructions.

3. Transfer the juice to a liquidizer and add the
   linseeds and frozen fruit. Blend until smooth,
   then pour into a glass and garnish with mint
   and an extra sprinkle of linseeds.

MAKES : 350ML

Preparation time: **5 minutes**

Sweet potato breakfast drink

3 sweet potatoes, halved and sliced

4 carrots

1 onion, peeled and quartered

2 cloves of garlic, peeled

parsley, to garnish

1. Reserve one of the sweet potatoes and process the rest through an electronic juicer with the carrots, onion and garlic.

2. Dice the reserved sweet potato and put it in a saucepan with the juice and a pinch of salt.

3. Cover with a lid and cook over a medium heat for 15 minutes or until the sweet potato is tender.

4. Blend until smooth in a liquidizer.

5. Serve hot or chilled.

Light bites and lunches

Embracing a dairy-free diet can sometimes be daunting, especially when you have to forget old classics. Whether you are intolerant to dairy or trying to cut it from your diet for other reasons, this chapter has a wide variety of recipes to entice everyone.

If some of your most favourite lunches contain dairy, do not despair. Experiment instead with tasty new recipes!

The Tomato and Lentil Soup is vitamin-rich and will warm you up on a cold day. Alternatively, the Roasted Roots or Red Pepper Tortilla is delicious and great fun to experiment with!

Whatever you choose, enjoy taking the time to prepare and cook it. When you first begin to cook dairy-free dishes, set aside some time at the weekend or in the evening to cook a few lunchtime recipes and see which you like the best. Then you can prepare and freeze your favourite dishes in individual portions, which are ready to grab and go when you're in a rush in the mornings.

Many of the recipes are easily portable too. Put the Kale Chips or Vegetable Skewers in a plastic container to take with you to work or on a day out.

SERVES: 4

Preparation time: **15 minutes**

Cooking time: **45 minutes**

Spicy potato wedges

800 g / 1 lb 12 oz potatoes, peeled and
  cut into wedges

1 tsp smoked paprika

1 tsp garlic powder

60 ml / 2 fl. oz / ¼ cup olive oil

1. Parboil the potatoes in boiling salted water
   for 5 minutes, then drain well and leave to
   steam dry for 2 minutes.

2. Meanwhile, put the oil in a large roasting tin
   in the oven and heat it to 200°C (180°C fan) /
   400F / gas 6.

3. Mix the smoked paprika and garlic powder
   with ½ tsp of salt and pepper, then sprinkle
   the mixture evenly over the potatoes.
   Carefully tip the wedges into the roasting tin
   and turn to coat in the oil.

4. Bake the wedges for 45 minutes, turning
   every 15 minutes, until golden brown on the
   outside and fluffy within. Sprinkle with a
   little more salt and serve immediately.

SERVES: 6

Preparation time: **5 minutes**

Cooking time: **40 minutes**

Tomato and lentil soup

2 tbsp olive oil

1 red onion, finely chopped

2 cloves of garlic, crushed

200 g / 7 oz / 1 ⅓ cups red lentils

600 ml / 1 pint / 2 ½ cups tomato passata

1 litre / 1 pint 15 fl. oz / 4 cups
   vegetable stock

1. Heat the oil in a large saucepan and fry the onion for 5 minutes to soften without colouring. Add the garlic and lentils and fry for 5 more minutes.

2. Pour in the passata and stock, then bring to the boil and simmer for 30 minutes or until the lentils are starting to break down into a puree.

3. Taste the soup and adjust the seasoning with salt and black pepper before serving.

SERVES: 4

Preparation time: **30 minutes**

Cooking time: **4 minutes**

Sweet and sour chicken balls

75 g / 2 ½ oz / ½ cup plain (all-purpose) flour

75 g / 2 ½ oz / ½ cup cornflour (cornstarch)

1 tsp baking powder

1 tsp caster (superfine) sugar

1 tsp sesame oil

4 skinless chicken breasts, cut into
   bite-sized chunks

vegetable oil, for deep-frying

FOR THE SAUCE

125 ml / 4 ½ fl. oz / ½ cup pineapple juice

50 ml / 1 ¾ fl. oz / ¼ cup tomato ketchup

2 tbsp rice wine vinegar

2 tbsp light brown sugar

1 tsp soy sauce

1 tbsp cornflour (cornstarch)

1. To make the sauce, heat the pineapple juice, ketchup, vinegar, sugar and soy sauce together in a small saucepan. Slake the cornflour with 3 tbsp of cold water, then stir it into the saucepan. Continue to stir over a medium heat until the sauce simmers and thickens. Transfer to serving pots and leave to cool.

2. Sieve the flour, cornflour, baking powder and sugar together. Stir the sesame oil into 150 ml of cold water, then whisk it into the flour to form a batter.

3. Heat the oil in a deep fat fryer, according to the manufacturer's instructions, to a temperature of 180°C (350F).

4. Dip the chicken breast chunks in batter and deep fry for 4 minutes or until nicely browned.

5. Drain the chicken on plenty of kitchen paper and serve with the sweet and sour sauce for dipping.

SERVES: 4

Preparation time: **5 minutes**

Cooking time: **12 minutes**

Vegetable skewers

2 small courgettes (zucchini)

1 red pepper, cut into chunks

8 mushrooms, halved

1 red onion, cut into chunks

½ aubergine (eggplant), cut into chunks

60 ml / 2 fl. oz / ¼ cup olive oil

1. Thread the vegetables on to eight metal skewers.
2. Brush them with olive oil and season with salt and black pepper.
3. Cook the vegetables on a barbecue or under a hot grill for 12 minutes, turning regularly.

SERVES : 6

Preparation time: **20 minutes**

Cooking time: **2 minutes**

Breaded calamari

sunflower oil, for deep frying

50 g / 1 ¾ oz / ⅓ cup plain
(all-purpose) flour

2 eggs, beaten

150 g / 5 ½ oz / 1 cup fine dried
breadcrumbs

300 g / 10 ½ oz / 2 cups squid tubes,
cleaned and sliced into rings

1 spring onion (scallion), thinly shredded

lemon wedges and romesco sauce, to serve

1. Heat the oil in a deep fat fryer, according to
   the manufacturer's instructions, to a
   temperature of 180°C (350F).

2. Put the flour, egg and breadcrumbs in three
   separate bowls. Working in small batches, dip
   the squid rings in the flour with one hand and
   shake off any excess.

3. Dip them in the egg with the other hand,
   then toss them into the breadcrumbs and use
   your floured hand to ensure they are
   thoroughly covered.

4. Fry the calamares in batches for 2 minutes or
   until golden brown.

5. Transfer the calamares to a kitchen paper
   lined bowl to blot away any excess oil, then
   transfer to a serving bowl and garnish with
   spring onions and lemon wedges. Serve
   immediately with romesco sauce.

SERVES : 4

Preparation time: **1 hour 40 minutes**

Cooking time: **15 minutes**

French fries

4 large Maris Piper potatoes, peeled and crinkle-cut into fries

sunflower oil, for deep-frying

ketchup, to serve

1. Soak the potatoes in cold water for 1 hour to reduce the starch.

2. Drain the chips and dry completely with a clean tea towel, then air-dry on a wire rack for 30 minutes.

3. Heat the oil in a deep fat fryer, according to the manufacturer's instructions, to a temperature of 130°C (265F). Par-cook the chips for 10 minutes so that they cook all the way through but don't brown. Drain the chips on plenty of kitchen paper to absorb the excess oil.

4. Increase the fryer temperature to 190°C (375F).

5. Return the chips to the fryer basket and cook for 4 minutes or until crisp and golden brown. Drain the chips of excess oil on kitchen paper and season with salt and pepper.

6. Serve immediately with ketchup for dipping.

SERVES : 4

Preparation time: **10 minutes**
Cooking time: **30 minutes**

Red pepper tortilla

60 ml / 2 fl. oz / ¼ cup olive oil

1 onion, thinly sliced

1 red pepper, quartered and thinly sliced

6 large eggs

1 tbsp flat leaf parsley, chopped

1. Heat half the oil in a non-stick frying pan over a medium-low heat. Fry the onion and red pepper with a pinch of salt and pepper for 15 minutes, stirring occasionally, until really soft and sweet.

2. Meanwhile, gently beat the eggs in a jug to break up the yolks. When the vegetables are ready, stir them into the eggs with the parsley and season with salt and pepper.

3. Wipe out the frying pan with a piece of kitchen paper and add the rest of the oil. Pour in the egg mixture and cook over a gentle heat for 6–8 minutes or until the egg has set round the outside, but the centre is still a bit soft.

4. Turn it out onto a plate, then slide it back into the pan and cook the other side for 4–6 minutes or until the egg is just set in the very centre.

5. Leave to cool for 5 minutes then cut into wedges and serve.

SERVES: 2

Preparation time: **10 minutes**

Cooking time: **20 minutes**

Fruity French toast

2 tbsp coconut oil

2 large apples, peeled, cored and cut
   into slices

75 g / 3 oz / ⅓ cup caster (superfine) sugar

2 large eggs

250 ml / 9 fl. oz / 1 cup soya milk

½ tsp vanilla extract

1 loaf of granary bread, cut into 8 thick slices

1. Preheat the oven to 190°C (170°C fan) / 375F / gas 5.

2. Melt the coconut oil in a heatproof pan over a medium heat.

3. Add the apples and half the caster sugar to the pan and leave to cook for 5-6 minutes, stirring every minute or so.

4. Once the apples are softened, remove them from the pan and keep them warm on a plate by covering them over with foil.

5. Whisk together the eggs and soya milk in a shallow bowl with the remaining sugar and vanilla extract.

6. One at a time, dip each side of all the slices of bread into the egg mixture. Position the egg-covered bread in rows on a non-stick griddle. Place in the oven for 4-6 minutes or until the bread is golden and toasted.

7. Take two plates and put four slices of the French toast on each one. Place the cooked apple on top and serve immediately.

SERVES: 1

Preparation time: **10 minutes**

Tuna bruschetta

180 g / 6 ½ oz tuna, tinned in water

1 tsp capers, chopped

2 spring onions (scallions), chopped

1 lemon, juice and zest

1 tsp extra virgin olive oil

2 slices of ciabatta or baguette, toasted

1 garlic clove, peeled

a handful of fresh parsley, chopped

1. In a bowl, mix together the tuna, capers, spring onions, lemon and olive oil. Combine fully and season with salt and black pepper to taste.

2. Rub the toasted bread with the garlic clove to flavour. Top with the tuna mixture and chopped parsley before serving.

MAKES: 6

Preparation time: **45 minutes**

Cooking time: **5 minutes**

Hot scotch eggs

8 medium eggs, 6 whole, 2 lightly beaten

400 g / 14 oz / 2 ⅔ cups good quality sausage meat

75 g / 2 ½ oz / ½ cup plain (all-purpose) flour

100 g / 3 ½ oz / 1 cup panko breadcrumbs

sunflower oil, for deep-frying

1. Put the six whole eggs in a pan of cold water then bring to the boil. Cover the pan, remove from the heat and leave to cook in the residual heat for 5 minutes.

2. Plunge the eggs into iced water for 5 minutes then peel off the shells.

3. Divide the sausage meat into six equal pieces. Flatten a portion of sausage meat onto your hand and put a boiled egg in the centre, then squeeze the meat around the outside to coat. Repeat with the other five boiled eggs.

4. Put the flour, beaten eggs and panko breadcrumbs in three separate bowls. Dip the scotch eggs alternately in flour, egg and breadcrumbs, then in egg and breadcrumbs again.

5. Heat the oil in a deep fat fryer, according to the manufacturer's instructions, to a temperature of 180°C (350F).

6. Lower the scotch eggs in the fryer basket and cook for 5 minutes or until crisp and golden brown.

7. Drain on plenty of kitchen paper, then cut in half and serve straight away.

SERVES: 4

Preparation time: **5 minutes**

Cooking time: **45 minutes**

Roasted roots

3 medium beetroot, peeled and quartered

2 golden beetroot, peeled and quartered

5 young carrots, peeled and halved lengthways

2 small red onions, thickly sliced horizontally

2 eating apples, halved

1 lemon, cut horizontally into 4 slices

1 bulb of garlic, halved horizontally

4 mild red chillies

50 ml / 1 ¾ fl. oz / ¼ cup olive oil

2 tbsp flat leaf parsley, chopped

2 tbsp dill, chopped

1. Preheat the oven to 200°C (180°C fan) / 400F / gas 6.
2. Mix all of the ingredients, except for the herbs, in a large roasting tin and season with salt and pepper.
3. Cover the tin with foil and roast for 25 minutes.
4. Stir well, then return to the oven uncovered for 20 minutes, stirring halfway through. If the beetroot are tender to the point of a knife, they are ready. If not, return to the oven for 10 minutes and test again.
5. Scatter the vegetables with herbs and serve immediately.

SERVES: 4

Preparation time: **5 minutes**

Cooking time: **30 minutes**

Kale chips

2 tbsp coconut oil, melted

100 g / 3 ½ oz / 3 cups kale, washed and dried

½ tsp sea salt flakes

1. Preheat the oven to 150°C (130°C fan) / 300F / gas 2.
2. Massage the oil into the kale and spread it out in a roasting tin.
3. Sprinkle with sea salt flakes and roast for 30 minutes, stirring every 10 minutes.
4. Serve immediately.

SERVES: 1

Preparation time: **5 minutes**

Avocado bruschetta

2 slices of ciabatta or granary bread, toasted

1 garlic clove, peeled

2 tbsp hummus

1 avocado, peeled, stoned and thinly sliced

1 lemon, juice

1 tsp extra virgin olive oil

a handful of fresh parsley, chopped

1. Rub the toasted bread with the garlic clove to flavour.

2. Spread the hummus over the toasted bread and layer the avocado slices on top.

3. Squeeze the lemon juice over the avocado to prevent browning then drizzle a little olive oil over the top.

4. Season with salt and freshly ground black pepper, then serve.

SERVES: 6

Preparation time: **10 minutes**

Cooking time: **20 minutes**

Fried potatoes

4 large floury potatoes, peeled and cut
   into chunks

sunflower oil, for deep frying

1. Heat the oil in a deep fat fryer, according
   to the manufacturer's instructions, to a
   temperature of 130°C (265F).

2. Lower the potatoes in the fryer basket and
   cook for 15 minutes so that they cook all the
   way through but don't brown. You may need
   to do this in batches so that the fryer isn't
   overcrowded.

3. Pull up the fryer basket then increase the
   fryer temperature to 190°C (375F). When the
   oil has come up to temperature, lower the
   fryer basket and cook the potatoes for
   5 minutes or until crisp and golden brown.

4. Line a large bowl with a few layers of kitchen
   paper and when the potatoes are ready, tip
   them into the bowl to remove any excess oil.

5. Serve with cocktail sticks to make it easier
   for dipping.

Main meals

Cooking the main meal of the day can be surprisingly easy on a dairy-free diet. Numerous ingredients are not dairy-related at all so your main concern is often to ensure you only use dairy-free fats for frying or roasting, such as coconut oil instead of butter.

Preparing a meal from scratch, with fresh ingredients that you have assembled yourself, is not only very rewarding but also eliminates any concerns about the contents of pre-packaged foods or ready-made meals. You can be sure exactly what you've added to the meal so you can stop worrying about any dairy products sneaking into your meal.

Take the time to plan your main meals. Work out what you want to cook, based on a good balance of main ingredients, herbs and spices. Add the ingredients to your shopping list and make sure you stick to it!

The recipes in this chapter are flavoursome and easy-to-follow. From Tomato Courgette and Rich Beef Stew to Cod and Cauliflower Curry or Spiced Salmon Cutlets, they are nutritious, delicious dishes.

SERVES: 4

Preparation time: **10 minutes**

Tomato courgetti

4 small courgettes (zucchini)

2 avocados, peeled, stoned and sliced

225 g / 8 oz / 1 ½ cups cherry
    tomatoes, halved

½ red onion, sliced

2 tbsp flat-leaf parsley, chopped

FOR THE DRESSING:

3 tbsp extra virgin olive oil

1 tbsp cider vinegar

1 tsp runny honey

1. Use a spiralizer to turn the courgettes into
   spaghetti-like ribbons.

2. Toss with the avocado, tomatoes, onion and
   parsley and divide between four bowls.

3. Make a simple dressing by shaking the oil,
   vinegar and honey together in a small jar.

4. Season with salt and pepper and serve with
   the salads.

SERVES: 4

Preparation time: **30 minutes**

Cooking time: **3 hours**

Rich beef stew

450 g / 1 lb / 3 cups braising steak, cut into
large chunks

2 tbsp plain (all-purpose) flour

2 tbsp olive oil

50 g / 1 ¾ oz / ¼ cup dairy-free butter

1 onion, finely chopped

2 carrots, diced

1 bay leaf

2 tsp sweet paprika

1 tbsp tomato puree

200 ml / 7 fl. oz / ¾ cup ruby port

250 ml / 9 fl. oz / 1 cup tomato passata

500 ml / 17 ½ fl. oz / 2 cups beef stock

4 medium potatoes, peeled and quartered

1. Season the braising steak with salt and pepper
   and dust all over with flour. Heat the oil and half
   the butter in a wide cast iron casserole dish over a
   high heat. Sear the steak all over in batches,
   transferring the pieces to a plate when they are
   well coloured.

2. Add the rest of the butter to the casserole dish and
   fry the onion, carrots and bay leaf for 10 minutes
   over a low heat, stirring regularly.

3. Stir in the paprika and tomato puree and cook
   for 1 minute, then add the port. Boil rapidly for
   3 minutes or until reduced by half, then stir in the
   passata and stock and return the beef to the pan.

4. Partially cover the pan with a lid and simmer
   very gently for 3 hours or until the beef is really
   tender and the sauce has reduced and thickened.

5. Towards the end of the cooking time, boil the
   potatoes in salted water until tender, then drain
   well. Discard the bay leaf and season the stew
   with salt and pepper, before stirring in the
   potatoes.

SERVES : 2

Preparation time: **10 minutes**
Cooking time: **8 minutes**

Mushroom, chicken and avocado salad

16 button mushrooms, halved

2 tbsp olive oil

2 large handfuls baby spinach

1 cooked chicken breast, thinly sliced

1 avocado, peeled, stoned and thinly sliced

18 cherry tomatoes

1 large handful rocket (arugula)

2 tbsp balsamic glaze

2 tsp sesame seeds

1. Heat a griddle pan until smoking hot.
   Toss the mushrooms with the oil and season
   with salt and pepper. Cook for 8 minutes,
   turning regularly, then leave to cool.

2. Arrange the spinach leaves on two plates.
   Toss the mushrooms with the chicken,
   avocado, tomatoes and rocket and divide
   between the plates.

3. Drizzle the salads with balsamic glaze
   and sprinkle with sesame seeds.

4. Serve immediately.

SERVES : 6

Preparation time: **15 minutes**

Cooking time: **4 minutes**

Hake goujons

800 g / 1 lb 12 oz / 5 ⅓ cups skinless
    boneless hake

50 g / 1 ¾ oz / ⅓ cup plain
    (all-purpose) flour

2 eggs, beaten

150 g / 5 ½ oz / 1 cup fine dried
    breadcrumbs

sunflower oil, for deep frying

1 lemon, halved

1. Cut the hake into 18 evenly sized goujons.
   Put the flour, egg and panko breadcrumbs
   in three separate bowls.

2. Dip the hake first in the flour, then in the
   egg, then in the breadcrumbs.

3. Heat the oil in a deep fat fryer, according
   to the manufacturer's instructions, to a
   temperature of 180°C (350F).

4. Lower the fish fingers in the fryer basket and
   cook for 4 minutes or until crisp and golden
   brown. You may need to cook them in two
   batches to avoid overcrowding the fryer, in
   which case keep the first batch warm in a
   low oven.

5. Line a bowl with layers of kitchen paper and,
   when they are ready, tip them into the bowl
   to remove any excess oil.

6. Sprinkle with a little sea salt to taste and
   squeeze over the juice of the lemon halves.

7. Serve immediately with fries.

Preparation time: **30 minutes**

Raising time: **1 hour**

Cooking time: **12 minutes**

Chicken and bacon pizza

200 g / 7 oz / 1 ⅓ cups strong white bread
  flour, plus extra for dusting

½ tsp easy blend dried yeast

1 tsp caster (superfine) sugar

½ tsp fine sea salt

1 tbsp olive oil, plus extra for drizzling

150 g / 5 ½ oz / 1 ½ cups dairy-free
  cheese, grated

1 cooked chicken breast, sliced

½ red pepper, deseeded and thinly sliced

4 rashers cooked streaky bacon,
  roughly chopped

1. Mix together the flour, yeast, sugar and salt and stir the oil into 140 ml of warm water.

2. Stir the liquid into the dry ingredients then knead on a lightly oiled surface for 10 minutes or until smooth and elastic.

3. Leave the dough to rest covered with oiled clingfilm for 1–2 hours until doubled in size.

4. Preheat the oven to 220°C (200° fan) / 425F / gas 7 and grease a non-stick baking tray.

5. Knead the dough for 2 more minutes then roll out thinly into an elongated oval. Transfer the base to the baking tray and top with dairy-free cheese, peppers and bacon. Season with plenty of black pepper.

6. Bake for 12 minutes or until the pizza dough is cooked through underneath.

7. Serve immediately.

SERVES: 4

Preparation time: **10 minutes**

Chicken and pepper salad

1 red pepper, thinly sliced

1 green pepper, thinly sliced

1 yellow pepper, thinly sliced

1 red onion, thinly sliced

cooked chicken breast, sliced

4 tsp extra virgin olive oil

1 handful unsalted peanuts

juice of 1 large lemon

1. Combine the slices of red pepper, green pepper, yellow pepper, red onion and chicken in a large mixing bowl and drizzle with the olive oil.

2. Add the peanuts and mix to combine the ingredients.

3. Divide up onto four plates and drizzle with the lemon juice.

4. This salad is perfect as a lunch or dinner.

SERVES: 4-6

Preparation time: **10 minutes**
Cooking time: **15 minutes**

Herby quinoa salad

300 g / 10 ½ oz / 1 ½ cups quinoa

1 red onion, finely sliced

1 small bunch of flat leaf parsley, chopped

1 small bunch of coriander, chopped

1 small bunch of fresh mint, chopped

2 lemons, zested and juiced

sea salt and freshly ground black pepper

1. Cook the quinoa as per the packet instructions.
2. Drain the quinoa thoroughly and spread over a baking tray to cool quickly and steam dry.
3. Once the quinoa has cooled, mix together with the other ingredients in a serving bowl and season with salt and black pepper to taste.
4. Serve immediately.

SERVES: 4

Preparation time: **5 minutes**

Cooking time: **35 minutes**

Cod and cauliflower curry

2 tbsp sunflower oil

1 onion, finely chopped

3 cloves of garlic, crushed

1 small cauliflower, cut into florets

2 tbsp curry powder

200 g / 7 oz / ¾ cup canned
   tomatoes, chopped

400 ml/ 14 fl. oz / 1 ²/₃ cup coconut milk

2 tbsp mango chutney

350 g / 12 ½ oz / 2 ⅓ cups skinless boneless
   cod loin, cut into bite-sized chunks

1 handful fresh curry leaves

rice and naan bread, to serve

1 handful coriander (cilantro) leaves

1. Heat the oil in a large saucepan and fry the onion for 8 minutes stirring occasionally.

2. Add the garlic and stir-fry for 2 minutes.

3. Add the cauliflower and cook for 2 minutes, then sprinkle over the curry powder and continue to cook for 1 minute.

4. Add the chopped tomatoes, coconut milk and mango chutney and bring to a gentle simmer.

5. Cook the curry for 15 minutes, stirring occasionally. Add the cod and curry leaves and cook for 5 minutes or until the cod is just cooked and starting to flake.

6. Season to taste with salt and pepper, then serve with rice and naan bread, garnished with coriander.

Preparation time: **20 minutes**

Cooking time: **10 minutes**

Red quinoa bowl

150 g / 5 ½ oz / ¾ cup red quinoa

1 spring onion, very finely chopped

½ tsp fresh root ginger, finely grated

1 tbsp lime juice

2 tsp light soy sauce

1 tsp sesame oil

½ ripe avocado, peeled, stoned and sliced

1 hard-boiled egg, sliced

1 tomato, chopped

1. Put the quinoa in a saucepan with 150 ml water. Cover and simmer gently for 10 minutes, then leave to stand off the heat for another 15 minutes without lifting the lid.

2. Stir the spring onion, ginger, lime juice, soy and sesame oil together, then stir it into the quinoa.

3. Transfer the mixture to a warm bowl and top with avocado, egg and tomato.

4. Season generously with black pepper and serve immediately.

SERVES: 4

Preparation time: **30 minutes**
Cooking time: **2 hours**

Slow cooker red pepper risotto

2 tbsp olive oil

1 onion, finely chopped

2 red peppers, finely chopped

2 cloves of garlic, finely chopped

1 tsp smoked paprika

300 g / 10 ½ oz / 1 ½ cups risotto rice

2 medium tomatoes, finely chopped

150 ml / 5 ½ fl. oz / ²/₃ cup dry white wine

750 ml / 1 pints 5 ½ fl. oz / 3 cups
    vegetable stock

50 g / 1 ¾ oz / 1 ½ cups rocket (arugula)

50 g / 1 ¾ oz / ½ cup dairy-free cheese,
    finely grated

1 lemon, cut into wedges

1. Heat the oil in a frying pan and fry the onion
   and peppers over a low heat for 18 minutes.
   Add the garlic and paprika and stir-fry for
   2 minutes.

2. Add the rice and stir over a low heat for
   3 minutes to toast it, then pour in the wine
   and add the tomato and bubble for 2 minutes.

3. Scrape the contents of the pan into a slow
   cooker, add the stock and stir well. Cover and
   cook on high for 2 hours or until the rice
   is cooked.

4. Stir well and season to taste, then spoon into
   four warm bowls and garnish with rocket,
   dairy-free cheese and lemon wedges.

Preparation time: **20 minutes**

Cooking time: **6 hours**

Slow cooker lamb and red pepper stew

450 g / 1 lb / 2 cups lamb shoulder, cubed

2 tbsp olive oil

1 onion, finely chopped

3 red romano peppers, sliced

2 cloves of garlic, finely chopped

2 tsp fresh root ginger, finely chopped

2 red chillies (chilies), chopped

1 tsp paprika

1 tsp ground cumin

2 tbsp tomato puree

600 ml / 1 pint / 2 ½ cups lamb or
    vegetable stock

1. Season the lamb all over with salt and pepper. Heat the oil in a frying pan and sear the lamb on all sides, then transfer the pieces to a slow cooker.

2. Fry the onion and peppers in the frying pan for 5 minutes, then stir in the garlic, ginger and chillies and fry for another 5 minutes. Scrape the mixture into the slow cooker and add the spices, tomato puree and stock.

3. Cover and cook on medium for 6 hours, then adjust the seasoning with salt and pepper.

4. Ladle into warm bowls to serve.

SERVES: 2

Preparation time: **5 minutes**
Cooking time: **5 minutes**

Spiced salmon cutlets

2 tbsp dairy-free butter

2 salmon cutlets

1 tbsp flaked almonds

½ tsp fennel seeds

½ tsp cracked mixed peppercorns

½ tsp ground sumac

fennel or dill fronds, to garnish

toast, to serve

1. Heat the dairy-free butter in a large frying pan. Season the salmon with a little salt and sprinkle with the almonds, fennel seeds, peppercorns and sumac.

2. Fry the salmon for 2 minutes on each side or until golden brown.

3. Garnish the salmon with fennel or dill fronds and serve with hot toast.

SERVES: 4

Preparation time: **10-15 minutes**

Cooking time: **40-50 minutes**

Chicken and pea risotto

2 tbsp coconut oil

1 shallot, finely chopped

2 cloves of garlic, minced

200 g / 7 oz / 1 cup short-grain rice

110 ml / 4 fl. oz / ½ cup dry white wine

1 l / 1 pint 16 fl oz / 4 cups hot chicken stock

2 chicken breasts, pre-cooked and cubed

75 g / 2 ½ oz / ½ cup frozen peas

1. Heat the coconut oil in a large, shallow saucepan over a medium heat.

2. Add the shallot, garlic and a little salt, sweating for 4–5 minutes until fully softened.

3. Add the rice and cook for 2–3 minutes, stirring frequently. Then add the dry white wine and let it reduce by half.

4. Pour the chicken stock into the rice then stir every minute or so for 30-35 minutes until the rice fully absorbs the liquid. Around 25 minutes into this cooking time, add the frozen peas, which will defrost and cook in the remaining 5-10 minutes.

5. Once the rice is plump and tender, stir through the chicken, then season to taste.

6. Spoon into bowls and serve.

SERVES: 4

Preparation time: **5 minutes**

Cooking time: **10 minutes**

Kimchi fried rice

2 tbsp vegetable oil

1 small onion, finely chopped

2 cloves of garlic, crushed

1 red pepper, deseeded, quartered and sliced

200 g / 7 oz / 1 ¾ cups kimchi, chopped

500 g / 17 ½ oz / 3 cups jasmine rice, cooked and cooled

2 tbsp light soy sauce

2 tsp sesame oil

1 small bunch Chinese chives, cut into short lengths

1. Heat the vegetable oil in a large wok and fry the onion and garlic or 2 minutes.

2. Add the red pepper and fry for 2 minutes.

3. Add the kimchi and rice and stir-fry until piping hot – this should take about 4 minutes.

4. Season the rice with soy sauce, sesame oil and black pepper, then serve immediately, garnished with Chinese chives.

5. Delicious served with fried chicken or beef.

SERVES : 4

Preparation time: **10-15 minutes**

Cooking time: **10 minutes**

Salmon steaks with salad

4 x 150 g / 5 oz salmon steaks

2 tbsp olive oil

2 handfuls mixed green leaf salad

1 pinch of micro herbs

1 tbsp flaked almonds (slivers)

1. Preheat the oven to 220°C (200°C fan) / 425F / gas 7.

2. Sit the salmon on a baking tray and drizzle with olive oil and season liberally with salt and pepper.

3. Roast for around 10 minutes or until firm to the touch.

4. Meanwhile, arrange the mixed salad leaves on the plate.

5. Once the salmon is cooked, place it on top of the bed of salad leaves and sprinkle with the micro herbs and flaked almonds on top before serving.

SERVES: 4

Preparation time: **5 minutes**

Cooking time: **15-20 minutes**

Chicken salad

½ lemon, juiced

2 tbsp sweet chilli (chili) sauce

1 tsp fennel seeds, finely ground

2 tbsp extra virgin olive oil, plus extra
  for drizzling

4 skinless chicken breasts, cut into
  large chunks

2 handfuls green mixed leaf salad

8 cherry tomatoes, halved

¼ cucumber, thinly sliced

1 handful basil leaves, washed

1. Preheat the oven to 220°C (200°C fan) /
   425F / gas 7.

2. Mix the lemon juice, chilli sauce, fennel
   seeds and oil in a bowl. Add the chicken
   chunks to the bowl and stir until coated.

3. Spread the coated chicken out on a
   non-stick baking tray and roast in the
   oven for 15-20 minutes or until browned
   on the outside and fully cooked.

4. While the chicken is cooking, divide the
   salad leaves, halved tomatoes and cucumber
   slices between four plates and pour over a
   drizzle of olive oil.

5. Once cooked, arrange the chicken on top
   of the salad and garnish each plate with a
   few basil leaves.

Desserts

You may feel that going dairy-free means waving goodbye to the delights of desserts. But that definitely doesn't have to happen.

With so many milk and cream substitutes available, there are a whole variety of cakes, puddings and sweet treats that you can make. Don't forget the naturally dairy-free sorbets and fruit puddings that you can conjure up and enjoy too!

Different kinds of plant-based milks have their own characteristics, which will affect the taste of a recipe. Some milks have a natural thickness or creaminess that lends itself to dessert-making. Other milks are thinner or better for using in savoury dishes. Experiment and try them out – you will be able to work out which ones you prefer.

The recipes in this chapter take into account all types of plant-based milks and dairy substitutes, and have done the experimenting for you. However, you may have your own milks that you rely on for cooking and you will know yourself how well they work in doughs and batters.

From Lemon and Coconut Sorbet and One-crust Apple Pie to Slow Cooker Spiced Rhubarb or Chocolate and Cherry Trifles, you will be pleasantly surprised at the variety of dairy-free desserts!

SERVES: 8

Preparation time: **45 minutes**

Freezing time: **4 hours**

Strawberry cheesecake

250 g / 9 oz / 1 ½ cups medjool dates, stoned

225 g / 8 oz / 1 ¾ cups walnuts, chopped

250 g / 9 oz / 1 ¾ cups raw cashew nuts, soaked overnight

400 ml / 14 fl. oz / 2 cup canned coconut milk, chilled, unopened

1 ½ lemons, juiced and zest finely grated

75 g / 2 ½ oz ¼ cup runny honey

150 g / 5 oz / 1 cup strawberries, plus more to decorate

1. Soak the dates in warm water for 10 minutes, then drain and transfer to a food processor. Add the chopped walnuts and pulse until it forms a dough. Line a 20 cm (8 in) round spring-form cake tin with cling film, then press this mixture into the base.

2. Drain the cashews and put them in the food processor. Open the can of coconut milk upside down. Discard the watery layer. Scoop the thick creamy layer into the processor. Add the lemon juice, zest and honey.

3. Blend until smooth, pausing occasionally to scrape down the sides. Scrape into the tin and level the top. Cover with cling film and freeze the cheesecake for at least 4 hours.

4. Remove from the freezer 20 minutes before serving.

5. Unmould the cheesecake and garnish the top by layering up the remaining strawberries, which can be sliced or halved, depending on your preferred decoration.

SERVES: 6

Preparation time: **20 minutes**

Cooking time: **10 minutes**

Chilling time: **2 hours**

chocolate cherry trifles

450 ml / 12 ½ fl. oz / 1 ¾ cups almond milk

4 large egg yolks

75 g / 2 ½ oz / ⅓ cup caster
   (superfine) sugar

1 tsp cornflour (cornstarch)

½ tsp almond extract

200 g / 7 oz / 2 cups dairy-free chocolate
   cake, crumbled

100 ml / 3 ½ fl. oz / ½ cup crème de cacao

150 g / 5 ½ oz / 1 cup black cherries
   in syrup, drained

1. Heat the almond milk until it starts to
   shimmer, but do not let it boil. Whisk the egg
   yolks with the caster sugar and cornflour
   until thick.

2. Gradually incorporate the hot milk, whisking
   all the time, then scrape the mixture back
   into the saucepan. Stir the custard over a low
   heat until it thickens then sit the bottom of
   the pan in a bowl of cold water to stop the
   cooking. Stir in the almond extract.

3. Mix the cake crumbs with half the crème de
   cacao and divide half between six dessert
   glasses. Pour over the custard, then chill in
   the fridge for 2 hours or until you're ready
   to serve.

4. Top the trifles with cherries and drizzle with
   the rest of the crème de cacao.

SERVES : 6

Preparation time: **30 minutes**

Cooking time: **1 hour**

Cooling time: **1 hour**

Berries and cherries pavlova

4 large egg whites

200 g / 7 oz / ¾ cup caster (superfine) sugar

1 tsp cornflour (cornstarch)

2 tsp raspberry vinegar

250 ml / 9 fl. oz / 1 cup thick soya yogurt

2 tbsp icing (confectioner's) sugar

½ tsp vanilla extract

100 g / 3 ½ oz / ²⁄₃ cup strawberries

100 g / 3 ½ oz / ²⁄₃ cup redcurrants

100 g / 3 ½ oz / ²⁄₃ cup red cherries

a few mint leaves

1. Preheat the oven to 140°C (120°C fan) / 275F / gas 1 and oil and line a baking tray with greaseproof paper.

2. Whisk the egg whites until stiff, then gradually whisk in half the sugar until the mixture is very shiny. Stir the cornflour into the vinegar, then fold it in with the remaining sugar. Spoon the mixture onto the baking tray and spread it into a circle with a palette knife.

3. Bake the meringue for 1 hour or until crisp on the outside, but still a bit chewy in the middle. Turn off the oven and leave the meringue to cool completely inside.

4. Mix the yogurt with the icing sugar and vanilla extract, then spoon it on top of the meringue. Cut half of the strawberries into quarters, leaving the rest whole, then arrange on top of the pavlova with the redcurrants and cherries. Garnish with mint leaves and serve immediately.

86 | Desserts

SERVES: 4

Preparation time: **15 minutes**

Cooking time: **5 minutes**

Freezing time: **4 hours**

Lemon and coconut sorbet

3 lemons, juiced and zest finely grated

200 g / 7 oz / 1 cup caster (superfine) sugar

125 ml / 4 ½ fl. oz / ½ cup coconut milk

a few mint leaves

1. Put the lemon juice, zest and sugar in a saucepan with 500 ml of water. Stir over a low heat until the sugar dissolves, then pass the mixture through a sieve into a measuring jug to remove the zest.

2. Stir in the coconut milk then chill in the fridge for 30 minutes.

3. Churn in an ice cream maker, according to the manufacturer's instructions, then freeze until ready to serve.

4. Alternatively, scrape the mixture into a plastic box with a lid and freeze for 2 hours. Scrape the semi-frozen mixture into a food processor and blend until smooth, then return it to the box and freeze for 1 hour. Whizz the mixture in the food processor again, then freeze until firm.

5. Scoop the sorbet into glasses and garnish with mint.

SERVES: 6

Preparation time: **25 minutes**

Cooking time: **40 minutes**

One-crust apple pie

1 large bramley apple, peeled, cored
   and chopped

1 tsp ground cinnamon

1 tsp cornflour (cornstarch)

3 tbsp caster (superfine) sugar

3 eating apples, peeled, cored and sliced

100 ml / 3 ½ fl. oz / ½ cup apricot jam (jelly)

FOR THE PASTRY

150 g / 5 ½ oz / ⅔ cup dairy-free butter,
   cubed and chilled

300 g / 10 ½ oz / 2 cups plain
   (all purpose) flour

1. Preheat the oven to 200°C (180°C fan) / 400F /
   gas 6.

2. To make the pastry, rub the dairy-free butter
   into the flour then add just enough cold water
   to form a pliable dough. Roll out the pastry
   into a large circle and transfer it to a
   baking tray.

3. Toss the chopped bramley with the cinnamon,
   cornflour and sugar, then pile it into the
   centre of the pastry, leaving an 8 cm (3 in)
   border around the outside. Top with the sliced
   apples, then fold the outside edge of the
   pastry up and over the top, crimping to hold
   it in place where necessary.

4. Bake the pie for 40 minutes or until the
   pastry is cooked through underneath. Heat
   the jam in a small saucepan, then spoon it
   over the top of the apples. Serve hot or cold.

SERVES: 8

Preparation time: **15 minutes**

Fresh fruit salad

4 nectarines, stoned and diced

3 kiwi fruit, peeled, halved and sliced

¼ seedless watermelon, peeled and diced

225 g / 8 oz / 1 ½ cups strawberries, quartered

225 g / 8 oz / 1 ½ cups blueberries

50 ml / 1 ¾ fl. oz / ¼ cup fresh orange juice

mint sprigs, to garnish

1. Toss all of the fruits together in a large mixing bowl, then pour over the orange juice.

2. The fruit salad will keep happily in the fridge for up to 4 hours before serving.

3. Spoon the salad into bowls and garnish each one with a sprig of mint.

SERVES: 4

Preparation time: **15 minutes**

Chilling time: **4 hours**

Chia, date and blueberry verrines

250 g / 9 oz / 1 ⅔ cups blueberries,
plus extra for sprinkling

4 medjool dates, stoned

250 ml / 9 fl. oz / 1 cup almond milk

100 g / 3 ½ oz / ½ cup chia seeds,
plus extra for sprinkling

1. Put the blueberries, dates and almond milk in a liquidizer and blend until smooth.

2. Stir in the chia seeds, then cover and refrigerate for 4 hours, stirring occasionally.

3. Return the mixture to the liquidizer and blend again.

4. Divide between four dessert glasses and sprinkle with a few more blueberries and the extra chia seeds before serving.

SERVES: 4

Preparation time: **10 minutes**

Chilling time: **2 hours**

Banana, avocado and cacao pudding

2 ripe bananas, peeled and sliced,
plus extra to garnish

2 ripe avocados, peeled, stoned and chopped

50 g / 1 ¾ oz / ½ cup cacao powder

3 tbsp manuka honey

50 ml / 1 ¾ fl. oz / ¼ cup soya milk

1 tsp ground cinnamon

2 tbsp cashew nuts, chopped

1. Put the banana, avocado, cacao, honey, soya milk and cinnamon in a food processor. Blend until very smooth, pausing to scrape down the sides occasionally, if necessary.

2. Scrape the mixture into four dessert glasses and chill for 2 hours.

3. Decorate the puddings with sliced banana and chopped cashew nuts for crunch.

SERVES : 2

Preparation time: **15 minutes**

Citrus salad

1 grapefruit

1 orange

2 blood oranges

1 handful of chopped mint leaves

1 pomegranate, seeds only

1 tsp raw organic honey

2 tsp extra virgin olive oil

a pinch of sea salt

1. To prepare the fruit, slice across the top and bottom of each before slicing off the peel, leaving as little of the white pith as possible. Slice into wheels, removing any pips, and arrange onto a plate.

2. Garnish the fruit with the chopped mint and pomegranate seeds.

3. Combine the honey and olive oil and drizzle over the salad before seasoning with sea salt.

SERVES: 4

Preparation time: **5 minutes**

Cooking time: **30 minutes**

Baked apples with sultanas and pine nuts

4 eating apples, halved and cored

100 g / 3 ½ oz / ½ cup sultanas

50 g / 1 ¾ oz / ½ cup pine nuts

2 tbsp manuka honey

¼ tsp ground cinnamon

1. Preheat the oven to 180°C (160°C fan) / 350F / gas 4.

2. Arrange the apples cut side up in a baking dish.

3. Mix the sultanas with the pine nuts, honey and cinnamon and pile on top of each apple half.

4. Cover with foil and bake in the oven for 30 minutes or until the apples are soft.

SERVES : 6

Preparation time: **5 minutes**

Cooking time: **2 hours**

Slow cooker spiced rhubarb

800 g / 1 lb 12 ½ oz forced rhubarb

2 star anise

1 cinnamon stick

1 vanilla pod, halved lengthways

3 slices fresh root ginger

50 g / 1 ¾ oz / ¼ cup stevia

1. Cut the rhubarb into short lengths and put it in a slow cooker with the spices.

2. Sprinkle over the stevia and 3 tablespoons of water, then cover and cook on medium for 2 hours.

3. Serve warm or leave to cool completely before chilling in the fridge.

SERVES: 4

Preparation time: **5 minutes**

Cooking time: **5 minutes**

Barbecued nectarines

6 nectarines

1. Cut the nectarines in half and remove the stones.
2. Cook them cut side down on a hot barbecue for 3 minutes, then turn them 90° and cook for another 2 minutes.
3. The nectarines are delicious served hot from the barbecue with ice cream.

SERVES : 4

Preparation time: **15 minutes plus chilling**

Fruit jelly pots

125 g / 4 ½ oz / 1 cup strawberry jelly cubes

600 ml / 1 pint 2 fl. oz / 2 ²/₃ cups
  boiling water

250 g / 9 oz / 2 cups raspberries, washed

250 g / 9 oz / 2 cups blackberries, washed

1. Place the jelly cubes in a heatproof jug
   and pour over a third of the boiling water.
   Stir until the cubes have dissolved.

2. Top up the jug with the rest of the water
   and leave to cool for a few minutes.

3. Fill four heatproof dessert pots with a
   handful of blackberries and a handful
   of raspberries and then pour over the
   jelly liquid.

4. Place the filled dessert pots in the fridge
   until set.

5. These desserts will keep in the fridge for
   2-3 days.

SERVES: 8

Preparation time: **5 minutes**
Cooking time: **10 minutes**

Chocolate dessert pots

300 g / 10 oz / 2 cups dairy-free dark
   chocolate, chopped

4 tbsp agave nectar

500 g / 18 oz / 2 ½ cups silken tofu, cubed

2 tbsp hot water

1. Melt the chocolate in a bain-marie by setting a heatproof bowl containing the chocolate over a simmering saucepan of water.

2. Once fully melted, remove the chocolate from the heat and leave to cool for a couple of minutes before scraping into a food processor.

3. Add the agave nectar, silken tofu and hot water to the processor and blend according to the manufacturer's instructions until the mixture is smooth and creamy.

4. Spoon the chocolate dessert into dessert pots or glasses and chill before serving.

5. Delicious served with berries or garnish with a sprig of mint.

Treats

It can be challenging to stick to three meals per day with no treats or snacks in between. Many traditional snack items can be the worst for containing dairy ingredients – chocolate bars, biscuits and even some cereal bars contain various dairy-based ingredients.

As you perfect and grow accustomed to your dairy-free diet, you may become an expert at choosing from the limited dairy-free items available at motorway service stations or coffee shops. However, it is even better if you can make these handy treats and snacks yourself, as you will know exactly what they do and do not contain.

From indulgent Chocolate and Marshmallows Brownies or Hazelnut Cookies to delicious Banana Loaf Cake or Mini Meringues, these dairy-free treats can be made in larger batches, if desired, and stored or frozen so that you always have something to hand when you head out of the house or get a sudden hunger pang.

MAKES: 9

Preparation time: **45 minutes**

Cooking time: **35 minutes**

Chilling time: **2 hours**

Chocolate marshmallow brownies

100 g / 3 ½ oz / ⅔ cup dairy-free dark chocolate (min. 70% cocoa solids), chopped

85 g / 3 oz / ¾ cup unsweetened cocoa powder, sifted

225 g / 8 oz / 1 cup coconut oil

450 g / 1 lb / 2 ½ cups light brown sugar

4 large eggs

110 g / 4 oz / 1 cup self-raising flour

FOR THE TOPPING

110 ml / 4 fl. oz / ½ cup canned coconut milk

150 g / 5 ½ oz / 1 cup dairy-free dark chocolate (min. 70% cocoa solids), finely chopped

2 tbsp coconut oil

75 g / 2 ½ oz / 1 ¼ cups mini marshmallows

1. Preheat the oven to 160°C (140°C fan) / 325F / gas 3 and oil and line a 20 cm (8 in) square cake tin with greaseproof paper.

2. Melt the chocolate, cocoa and coconut oil together in a saucepan, then leave to cool a little.

3. Whisk the sugar and eggs together with an electric whisk for 3 minutes or until very light and creamy. Pour in the chocolate mixture and sieve over the flour, then fold it all together until smooth.

4. Scrape into the tin and bake for 35 minutes or until the outside is set, but the centre is still quite soft. Leave to cool completely.

5. To make the topping, put the coconut milk in a small saucepan and heat it gently. Meanwhile, put the chocolate and coconut oil in a mixing bowl. When the coconut milk starts to simmer, pour it over the chocolate in the bowl. Leave to stand for 30 seconds, then stir gently to form a ganache.

6. Spread all but 3 tbsp of the ganache over the brownie and top with marshmallows. Drizzle over the rest of the ganache, then refrigerate for 2 hours or until firm.

MAKES : 2 OF EACH FLAVOUR

Preparation time: **15 minutes**

Freezing time: **4 hours**

Pure juice ice lollies

RED LOLLIES:

2 beetroot, quartered

2 red apples, quartered

150 g / 5 ½ oz / 1 cup raspberries

YELLOW LOLLIES:

150 g / 5 ½ oz / 1 cup butternut
    squash, cubed

1 yellow pepper, quartered

2 mangoes, stoned and cut into chunks

GREEN LOLLIES:

3 kiwi fruit, quartered

½ head broccoli, broken into florets

½ honeydew melon, peeled and cut
    into chunks

1. For each type of lolly, process the ingredients
   through an electronic juicer, according to the
   manufacturer's instructions.

2. Divide each type of juice between two holes of
   a 6-hole ice lolly maker.

3. Freeze for **4 hours** or until solid before
   unmoulding and serving.

MAKES: 35

Preparation time: **30 minutes**

Cooking time: **30 minutes**

Chocolate flapjack bites

2 ripe bananas

100 ml / 3 ½ fl. oz / ⅓ cup raw honey

100 g / 3 ½ oz / ½ cup dairy-free butter

450 g / 1 lb / 4 ½ cups rolled porridge oats

200 g / 7 oz / 1 ⅓ cups dairy-free dark
chocolate (min. 70% cocoa solids)

1. Preheat the oven to 190°C (170°C fan) / 375F /
   gas 5 and grease and line a 20 cm x 28 cm
   (8 in x 11 in) tray bake tin with greaseproof
   paper.

2. Put the bananas in a blender with the honey
   and dairy-free butter and blend until smooth.
   Stir in the oats then spoon into a greased
   baking tin and level the surface.

3. Bake for 30 minutes or until golden brown
   and cooked through.

4. Cut into 4 cm (1 ½ in) squares while still
   warm, but leave to cool completely before
   removing from the tin.

5. Melt the dark chocolate in a microwave or
   bain-marie, then dip each flapjack and leave
   to set on a sheet of greaseproof paper.

MAKES : 12

Preparation time: **20 minutes**
Cooking time: **20 minutes**

Hazelnut cookies

100 g / 3 ½ oz / 1 cup rolled
    buckwheat flakes

150 g / 5 ½ oz / 1 cup buckwheat flour

75 g / 2 ½ oz / ⅔ cup hazelnuts, chopped

50 g / 1 ¾ oz / ½ cup desiccated coconut

100 g / 3 ½ oz / ½ cup coconut sugar

½ tsp bicarbonate of (baking) soda

125 ml / 4 ½ fl. oz / ½ cup coconut oil, melted

1. Preheat the oven to 180°C (160° fan) / 350F /
   gas 4 and line a large baking tray with
   greaseproof paper.

2. Put all of the ingredients in a food processor
   and pulse until it forms a dough, adding a few
   tbsp of water if necessary.

3. Roll the mixture into walnut-sized balls, then
   flatten them onto the baking tray.

4. Transfer the tray to the oven and bake for
   20 minutes, turning round halfway though.
   Leave to cool completely on the tray
   before serving.

MAKES : 12

Preparation time: **15 minutes**

Chilling time: **1 hour**

Oat and flax cacao balls

100 g / 3 ½ oz / 1 cup rolled porridge oats

25 g desiccated coconut

100 g / 3 ½ oz / ¾ cup pistachio nuts

2 tbsp manuka honey

50 g / 1 ¾ oz / ¼ cup smooth dairy-free peanut butter

2 tbsp coconut oil

30 g / 1 oz / ¼ cup pure cacao powder

8 medjool dates, stoned and chopped

2 tbsp flax seeds

1. Put the oats and pistachios in a food processor and blitz until finely ground. Add the rest of the ingredients and pulse to form a dough.

2. Divide the dough into 12 equal pieces and roll each one into a ball.

3. Chill in the fridge for 1 hour before serving.

SERVES: 8

Preparation time: **15 minutes**

Cooking time: **50 minutes**

Banana loaf cake

4 very ripe bananas

100 g / 3 ½ oz / ½ cup soft light brown sugar

2 large eggs

125 ml / 4 ½ fl. oz / ½ cup sunflower oil

225 g / 8 oz / 1 ½ cups plain
(all-purpose) flour

3 tsp baking powder

1. Preheat the oven to 160°C (140°C fan) / 325F / gas 3 and line a loaf tin with greaseproof paper.

2. Mash three of the bananas roughly with a fork then whisk in the sugar, eggs and oil.

3. Sieve the flour and baking powder into the bowl and add stir just enough to evenly mix all of the ingredients together.

4. Scrape the mixture into the loaf tin. Cut the final banana in half lengthways and press it into the top. Bake for 50 minutes or until a skewer inserted comes out clean.

5. Transfer the cake to a wire rack and leave to cool completely.

MAKES : 2 X 250 ML

Preparation time: **5 minutes**

Blueberry coconut milkshake

350 g / 12 ½ oz / 2 cups pineapple,
    cut into chunks

350 g / 12 ½ oz / 2 ⅓ cups frozen
    blueberries

200 ml / 7 fl. oz / ¾ cup coconut milk

6 fresh blueberries, to garnish

1. Process the pineapple through an electronic juicer, according to the manufacturer's instructions.
2. Transfer the juice to a liquidizer with the frozen blueberries and coconut milk. Blend until smooth, then pour into two glasses.
3. Garnish each smoothie with three blueberries and serve with a straw.

MAKES: 24

Preparation time: **20 minutes**

Cooking time: **1 hour**

Mini meringues

4 large egg whites

100 g / 3 ½ oz / ½ cup caster (superfine) sugar

1. Preheat the oven to 140°C (120°C fan) / 275F / gas 1 and oil and line a large baking tray with greaseproof paper.

2. Whisk the egg whites with an electric whisk until stiff, then gradually whisk in half the caster sugar until the mixture is very shiny. Fold in the remaining caster sugar with a large metal spoon, being careful to retain as much air as possible.

3. Spoon the meringue into a piping bag fitted with a large star nozzle and pipe small rosettes onto the baking tray.

4. Transfer the tray to the oven and bake for 1 hour. Turn off the oven and leave the meringues to cool slowly inside before serving.

MAKES : 8

Preparation time: **30 minutes**
Cooking time: **10 minutes**

Vanilla-glazed fruit kebabs

1 star fruit, thickly sliced

2 slices fresh pineapple, cut into wedges

1 banana, sliced with skin left on

1 kiwi fruit, halved and thickly sliced

½ papaya, cut into large chunks

1 pear, halved and thickly sliced

8 strawberries

50 g / 1 ¾ oz / ¼ cup dairy-free butter

2 tbsp maple syrup

1 vanilla pod, halved lengthways

2 tbsp mixed seeds

1. Soak eight wooden skewers in cold water for 20 minutes.

2. Thread the fruit onto the skewers and set aside.

3. Put the dairy-free butter and maple syrup in a small saucepan. Scrape the seeds from the vanilla pod and add them to the pan, then warm it gently until the butter melts.

4. Brush half the vanilla glaze over the kebabs, then cook them over a medium-hot barbecue for 4 minutes on each side.

5. Brush the kebabs with the rest of the vanilla glaze and sprinkle with seeds.

MAKES: 8

Preparation time: **10 minutes**

Chilling time: **1 hour**

Cacao goji berry fudge bars

1 cup medjool dates, stoned

75 g / 2 ½ oz / ½ cup goji berries

2 tbsp hulled hemp seeds

125 ml / 4 fl. oz / ½ cup coconut milk

150 g / 5 ½ oz / 1 cup dairy-free dark chocolate (min. 70% cocoa solids), chopped

2 tbsp cacao powder

175 g / 6 oz / ¾ cup smooth dairy-free peanut butter

1. Soak the dates in warm water for 15 minutes. Meanwhile, line a 23 cm x 13 cm (9 in x 5 in) rectangular cake tin with greaseproof paper.

2. Bring the coconut milk to simmering point. Put 50 g of the chocolate in a bowl, then pour over the coconut milk and wait for 30 seconds. Stir slowly together until smooth.

3. Transfer the chocolate mixture to the liquidizer and add the drained dates, cacao and dairy-free peanut butter. Blend until very smooth.

4. Scrape the mixture into the prepared tin and freeze for 2 hours.

5. Meanwhile, put the goji berries in a liquidizer and blitz until very finely chopped. Mix with the hemp and set aside.

6. Melt the rest of the chocolate in a bain-marie or microwave. Pour it over the fudge and level with a palate knife, then sprinkle with the goji hemp mix. Cut it into eight bars, then return to the freezer for 30 minutes before serving.

SERVES : 2

Preparation time: **5 minutes**

Kiwi and mango fruit salad

2 ripe mangos, peeled and cubed

6 ripe kiwis, peeled and cubed

1 lemon, cut in half

2 handfuls mint leaves, slightly crushed

1. Put even amounts of the kiwi and mango cubes in two bowls.

2. Squeeze over the juice from the halves of lemon, ensuring you catch any pips. This will prevent the fruit from browning.

3. Decorate the fruit salad with mint leaves.

4. Serve immediately or keep refrigerated in an airtight container until needed.

SERVES: 4

Preparation time: **15 minutes**

Homemade guacamole

2 red chillies (chili)

½ red onion

3 ripe avocados

2 garlic cloves, minced

1 bunch fresh coriander (cilantro)

6 cherry tomatoes

2 limes, juice and zest

pinch of salt

1. Deseed and finely chop the red chillies and finely dice the red onion.

2. Peel and destone the avocado and mash in a bowl with the back of a fork. Mix in the chopped chilli, garlic and onion.

3. Finely chop some of the coriander stalks and roughly chop the leaves before adding to the avocado along with the chopped and deseeded tomatoes. Add the lime juice and zest and season to taste with the salt.

4. Serve alongside plain, dairy-free tortilla chips for a great snack.

Meal plans and diary

One of the hardest aspects of a dairy-free diet is being limited in your choices as you browse the shelves of the supermarket. So many items are out of bounds because of their ingredients.

The key to success is to find exciting substitutes for much-loved foods. Don't simply cut out essentials but replace them with alternatives that may soon become your chosen taste-bud tantalisers when you're in need of a treat. Experiment with the recipes in the previous sections so that mealtimes don't become a chore. Food is meant to be fun, as well as fuel for a healthy body, full of vitality.

Don't forget to plan

Most people find that organisation is paramount in making their dairy-free days run smoothly and easily. Take time at the weekend to flick through the recipes and fill in a meal plan for the week ahead. Choose two or three lunches and make double the amount, which will then see you through the week. Decide on your evening meals and make sure that you shop efficiently for the right ingredients so nothing is wasted.

It's important, too, that you don't deny yourself treats. The chances are that your decision to ditch dairy will be a long-term plan, so you need to know how to choose treats that fit the bill. Bake in batches and freeze any excess, so you always have something tasty for that between-meals lull, or when you're on the road. Don't ever think that dairy-free equals fun-free – it's up to you how much you enjoy your food!

Week 1

	Breakfast	Lunch	Dinner	Snacks
Monday				
Tuesday				
Wednesday				
Thursday				
Friday				
Saturday				
Sunday				

How I feel (at the start of the week)

Improvements felt during the week

Symptoms I'm aiming to clear

New foods tried

Week 2

	Breakfast	Lunch	Dinner	Snacks
Monday				
Tuesday				
Wednesday				
Thursday				
Friday				
Saturday				
Sunday				

How I feel (at the start of the week)

Improvements felt during the week

Symptoms I'm aiming to clear

New foods tried

Week 3

	Breakfast	Lunch	Dinner	Snacks
Monday				
Tuesday				
Wednesday				
Thursday				
Friday				
Saturday				
Sunday				

How I feel (at the start of the week)

Improvements felt during the week

Symptoms I'm aiming to clear

New foods tried

Week 4

	Breakfast	Lunch	Dinner	Snacks
Monday				
Tuesday				
Wednesday				
Thursday				
Friday				
Saturday				
Sunday				

How I feel (at the start of the week)

Improvements felt during the week

Symptoms I'm aiming to clear

New foods tried

Shopping list

To begin with, you will find that you need to refill your cupboards with a selection of new, dairy-free items. Plan your meals and make a list as you go along, buying new store-cupboard essentials as well as the staple ingredients for your chosen recipes.

Store-cupboard items

Cooking oil – sunflower, olive, coconut

Dairy-free chocolate (many dark chocolates with a minimum of 70% cocoa solids are dairy-free)

Carob powder, solid chocolate

Cocoa (cacao) powder (pure/raw)

Honey and syrup (maple, agave nectar)

Polenta (a good alternative to breadcrumbs)

Quinoa (high in calcium)

Millet (high in protein)

Beans – aduki, black-eyed, borlotti, butter, cannellini, haricot (good for adding creaminess and texture)

Lentils and chickpeas (garbanzo beans)

Dried mushrooms

Tinned fish

Seeds – pumpkin, sunflower, sesame, linseed

Nuts – all types, unless you're allergic

Passata

Pasta and noodles

Rice (brown, white, basmati, arborio)

Garlic

Spices

Herbs

Tomato purée

Cornflour (cornstarch)

Stock cubes

Flour

Fridge/freezer and other items

Dairy-free milk/cream – soya, nut, rice

Dairy-free spread – sunflower, soya

Nut butter – peanut, almond, cashew

Dairy-free yogurt, cream, cheese, ice cream

Meat

Fish

Seafood

Tofu

Eggs

Vegetables

Potatoes

Fruit

Dairy-free biscuits

Dairy-free breadcrumbs

Root ginger

Lemongrass

Tahini

Fail-safe food guide

At first, shopping will be a time-consuming task as you scour the ingredients lists for pitfalls. Keep a note here of tried-and-trusted products to save yourself valuable minutes on each trip. Note down items that have caught you out with hidden milk-based products, too. But always remember to revisit the items periodically in case the recipe or preparation conditions change.

Free-from items

No-go items

Dairy-free me!

So, how is it going? Are you reaping the benefits of a fresh and healthy diet, without any of the symptoms that prompted you to ditch dairy in the first place?

As you explore and experiment with the recipes in this book, you should find that you grow in confidence and enjoy the whole experience of eating so much more – especially without the fear of adverse side effects after a meal or a treat. Maybe you have extended the dairy-free diet to your whole family so that you can cook one meal for all, leaving your loved ones also feeling brighter and lighter. The next step is to share your culinary creations with friends and see if they even notice the absence of dairy ingredients.

A new lifestyle

The joy of the whole process is that there is no 'point of return', where you wonder what you're missing – because you aren't missing anything. With luck, you won't feel the need to reintroduce dairy produce, but if you do, take small steps and monitor your body's reaction after each new food.

Be prepared to knock out items at the first sign of unwanted feelings of tiredness, worsening of your skin or stomach problems.

After a while, you should have a newfound love of food in all its glory, with far fewer processed and packaged products. You will discover that there is no room in your food diary for dairy items, as you are now buying, cooking and eating so many new or forgotten foods that had been forced out of your meal plans. It's a whole new you!

Diet consultant: Jo Stimpson

Written by: Lisa Regan

Picture Credits

Dreamstime: 28 Svetlanak, 112 Monkey Business Images, 122b Isebastian, 124t Charlieaja, 127 Epicstock

Shutterstock: 122t Kovaleva_Ka, 123 Sergiy Zavgorodny, 124b Shawn Hempel

All other imagery: © iStock / Getty